The Booktime Book of Fantastic First Poems

This **Booktime** book belongs to

. . . .

www.booktime.org.uk

PUFFIN BOOKS
Published by the Penguin Group: London, New York, Australia, Canada, India,
Ireland, New Zealand and South Africa
Penguin Books Ltd, Registered Offices: 80 Strand, London WC2R 0RL, England

puffinbooks.com

First published by Viking 1999
Published in Puffin Books under the title *The Puffin Book of Fantastic First Poems* 2000
This abridged edition published on behalf of Pearson
in association with Booktrust for Booktime 2008
1 3 5 7 9 10 8 6 4 2

The moral right of the authors and illustrators has been asserted
Made and printed in China by Absolutely Trading Ltd

British Library Cataloguing in Publication Data
A CIP catalogue record for this book is available from the British Library

ISBN 978-0-141-32553-8

CONTENTS

HopalooKangaroo *Illustrated by Emily Bolam*

Higglety, Pigglety, Pop *Illustrated by Nick Sharratt*

ACKNOWLEDGEMENTS

Booktime gratefully acknowledges the waiving of fees and royalties for this edition.

'Cat's Note' and 'HopalooKangaroo' from *We Animals Would Like a Word With You* by John Agard (The Bodley Head, 1996) and 'No Hickory No Dickory No Dock' from *No Hickory No Dickory No Dock* (Viking, 1991) – all by kind permission of John Agard c/o Caroline Sheldon Literary Agency; 'My Name is …' by Pauline Clarke from *Silver Bells and Cockle Shells*, © Pauline Clarke 1962, reproduced by permission of Curtis Brown Ltd, London; 'Pleas-e!' from *The Jungle Sale* (Viking, 1988) by June Crebbin, 'Ready, Steady, Moo!' from *Cows Moo, Cars Toot* (Viking, 1995) by June Crebbin, copyright © June Crebbin 1988, 1992 & 1995, 'Snail' by John Drinkwater, out of copyright; 'Cats' by Eleanor Farjeon from *The Children's Bells* (OUP), reprinted by permission of David Higham Associates Ltd; 'Hen's Song' and 'Witch, Witch' by Rose Fyleman, reprinted by permission of The Society of Authors as the literary representative of the Estate of Rose Fyleman; 'Tiger' by Mary Ann Hoberman, copyright © 1959 by Mary Ann and Norman Hoberman, renewed 1987, 1998 by Mary Ann Hoberman, reprinted by permission of Gina Maccoby Literacy Agency and Harcourt, Inc.; extract from 'My Donkey' from *What is the Truth?* by Ted Hughes (Faber & Faber Ltd), reprinted by permission of the Estate of Ted Hughes; 'Honey Bear' by Elizabeth Lang from *Book of a Thousand Poems* (Evans Brothers, 1942), reprinted by permission of HarperCollins Publishers; 'Kitty' from *The Fed Up Family Album* by Doug MacLeod, reprinted by permission of Penguin Books Australia; 'Granny Goat' by Brian Moses from *Twinkle Twinkle Chocolate Bar* (Oxford University Press, 1991) © Brian Moses 1999, reprinted by permission of the poet; 'Don't Cry Caterpillar' from *No Hickory No Dickory No Dock* (Viking, 1991), reproduced with permission of Curtis Brown Ltd, London, on behalf of Grace Nichols, copyright Grace Nichols 1991; 'Roger was a Razor Fish' by Al Pittman from *Down By Jim Long's Stage*, published by Breakwater, St John's, Newfoundland, © the author 1976; 'Hey Diddle Diddle' from *Hairy Tales and Nursery Crimes* (Scholastic Books Ltd) by Michael Rosen, reprinted by permission of Scholastic Books Ltd; 'My Dad's Thumb' from *Mind Your Own Business* (Scholastic Books Ltd) by Michael Rosen © Michael Rosen, reprinted by permission of Scholastic Books Ltd; 'The Tickle Rhyme' by Ian Serraillier from *The Monster Horse* (Oxford University Press, 1950), copyright 1950, reprinted by permission of the Estate of Ian Serraillier; 'Nutter' from *Rabbiting On* by Kit Wright (Collins, 1978), reprinted by permission of the author; 'Little Bird' from *River Winding* by Charlotte Zolotow, copyright © 1970 by Charlotte Zolotow, reprinted by permission of S©ott Treimel New York.

HOPALOO-
KANGAROO

●●●●●●●●●

Animal Poems

HEN'S SONG

Chick, chick, come out of your shell.
I've warmed you long, and I've warmed you well;
The sun is hot and the sky is blue
Quick, chick, it's time you came through.

Rose Fyleman

ROGER WAS A RAZOR FISH

Roger was a razor fish
as sharp as he could be.
He said to Calvin Catfish,

'I'll shave you for a fee.'

'No thanks,'
said Calvin Catfish,
'I like me like I be.'
And with his whiskers
on his face
he headed out to sea.

Al Pittman

The Tickle Rhyme

'Who's that tickling my back?' said the wall.
'Me,' said a small
Caterpillar. 'I'm learning
To crawl.'

Ian Serraillier

Kitty

Look at pretty little Kitty
Gnawing on a bone!
How I wish she'd eat some fish
And leave my leg alone.

Doug MacLeod

CAT'S NOTE

How often can you take a poem
    and stroke it on your lap?

John Agard

A DRAGONFLY

When the heat of the summer
Made drowsy the land,
A dragonfly came
And sat on my hand.

With its blue jointed body
And wings like spun glass,
It lit on my fingers
As though they were grass.

Eleanor Farjeon

READY, STEADY – MOO!

It's peaceful here by the river,
All by ourselves in the sun,
Having a chew and a chat now and then,
Moving gently along.

But I'm not too keen on the hikers
That pass through our field each day,
One of them always waves a stick
In a menacing kind of way.

I'm not too keen on their children
Dashing all over the place,
Or their dogs, which run and nip at my heels
And yap in front of my face.

If only they'd just keep going,
If only they'd leave us alone,
Don't they know they're walking through
the middle of our home?

It's time we taught them a lesson,
Yes, but what can we do?
We could try giving voice to the way that we feel:

Ready, steady – MOO-OO-OO!

It's peaceful here by the river,
Now that the hikers have gone,
All by ourselves in the meadow again,
Flicking our tails in the sun.

June Crebbin

CATS

Cats sleep
Anywhere,
Any table,
Any chair,
Top of piano,
Window-ledge,
In the middle,
On the edge,
Open drawer,
Empty shoe,
Anybody's
Lap will do,
Fitted in a
Cardboard box,
In the cupboard
With your frocks –
Anywhere!
They don't care!
Cats sleep
Anywhere.

Eleanor Farjeon

DON'T CRY, CATERPILLAR

Don't cry, Caterpillar
Caterpillar, don't cry
You'll be a butterfly – by and by.

Caterpillar, please
Don't worry 'bout a thing

'But,' said Caterpillar,
'Will I still know myself – in wings?'

Grace Nichols

THE TADPOLE

Underneath the water-weeds,
    Small and black, I wriggle,
And life is most surprising!
    Wiggle! waggle! wiggle!
There's every now and then a most
    Exciting change in me,
I wonder, wiggle! waggle!
    What I shall turn out to be.

Elizabeth Gould

HOPALOOKANGAROO

If you can jigaloo
jigaloo
I can do
the jigaloo too
for I'm the jiggiest
jigaloo kangaroo

jigaloo all night through
jigaloo all night through

If you can boogaloo
boogaloo
I can do
the boogaloo too
for I'm the boogiest
boogaloo kangaroo

boogaloo all night through
boogaloo all night through

But bet you can't hopaloo
hopaloo
like I can do
for I'm the hoppiest
hopaloo kangaroo

hopaloo all night through
hopaloo all night through

Gonna show you steps
you never knew.
And guess what, guys?
My baby in my pouch
will be dancing too.

John Agard

SNAIL

Snail upon the wall,
Have you got at all
Anything to tell
About your shell?

Only this, my child –
When the wind is wild,
Or when the sun is hot,
It's all I've got.

John Drinkwater

TIGER

I'm a tiger
Striped with fur
Don't come near
Or I might Grrr
Don't come near
Or I might growl
Don't come near
Or I might
BITE!

Mary Ann Hoberman

HEY DIDDLE DIDDLE

Hey diddle, diddle,
The cat and the fiddle,
The cow jumped over the moon;
The little dog laughed
To see such fun,
And the dish ran away
with the chocolate biscuits.

Traditional, adapted by Michael Rosen

LITTLE BIRD

Little hurt bird
in my hand
your heart beats
like the pound of the sea
under the warmth
of your soft feathers.

Charlotte Zolotow

FIVE LITTLE OWLS

Five little owls in an old elm tree,
Fluffy and puffy as owls could be,
Blinking and winking with big round eyes
At the big round moon that hung in the skies:
As I passed beneath I could hear one say,
'There'll be mouse for supper, there will, today!'
Then all of them hooted, 'Tu-whit, tu-whoo
Yes, mouse for supper, hoo hoo, hoo hoo!'

Anon

MY DONKEY

His face is what I like.
And his head, much too big for his body – a toy head,
A great, rabbit-eared, pantomime head,
And his friendly rabbit face,
His big, friendly, humorous eyes – which can turn wicked,
Long and devilish, when he lays his ears back.

But mostly he's comical – and that's what I like.
I like the joke he seems.
Always just about to tell me. And the laugh,
The rusty, pump-house engine that cranks up laughter
From some long-ago, far-off, laughter-less desert –

The dry, hideous guffaw
That makes his great teeth nearly fall out.

Ted Hughes

WHISKY FRISKY

Whisky frisky,
Hipperty hop,
Up he goes
To the tree top!

Whirly, twirly,
Round and round,
Down he scampers
To the ground.

Furly, curly,
What a tail,
Tall as a feather,
Broad as a sail.

Where's his supper?
In the shell.
Snappy, cracky,
Out it fell.

Anon

HONEY BEAR

There was a big bear
Who lived in a cave;
His greatest love
Was honey.
He had twopence a week
Which he never could save,
So he never had
Any money.
I bought him a money box
Red and round,
In which to put
His money.
He saved and saved
Till he got a pound,
Then he spent it all
On honey.

Elizabeth Lang

No Hickory No Dickory No Dock

Wasn't me
Wasn't me
said the little mouse
I didn't run up no clock

You could hickory me
You could dickory me
or lock me in a dock

I still say
I didn't run up no clock

Was me who ran under your bed
Was me who bit into your bread
Was me who nibbled your cheese

But please please,
I didn't run up no clock
no hickory
no dickory
no dock.

John Agard

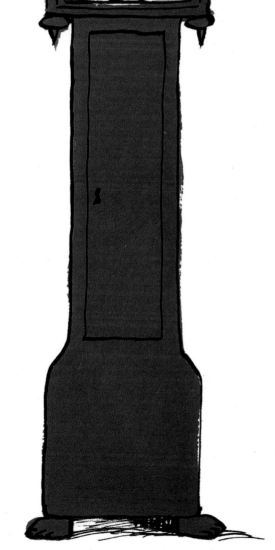

GRANNY GOAT

Eat anything
will granny goat,
handkerchiefs,
the sleeve of your coat,
sandwiches,
a ten pound note,
eat anything
will granny goat.

Granny goat
goes anywhere,
into the house
if you're not there,
follows you round,
doesn't care,
granny goat
goes anywhere.

Granny goat
will not stay
tied up
throughout the day,
chews the rope,
wants to play,
granny goat
won't stay

anywhere you
want her to,
she would rather be
with YOU!

Brian Moses

HIGGLETY, PIGGLETY, POP

Fun and Nonsense Poems

THE OLD MAN OF PERU

There was an old man of Peru,
Who dreamt he was eating his shoe.
    He woke in the night
    In a terrible fright,
And found it was perfectly true.

Anon

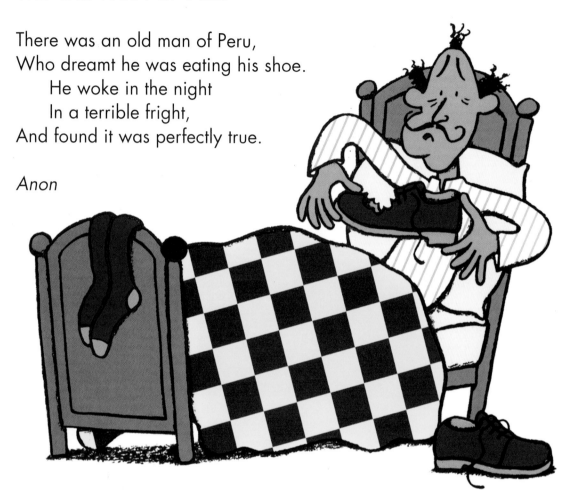

HIGGLETY, PIGGLETY, POP

Higglety, pigglety, pop!
The dog has eaten the mop;
The pig's in a hurry,
The cat's in a flurry,
Higglety, pigglety, pop!

Unknown

18

MY NAME IS ...

My name is Sluggery-wuggery
My name is Worms-for-tea
My name is Swallow-the-table-leg
My name is Drink-the-Sea
My name is I-eat-saucepans
My name is I-like-snails
My name is Grand-piano-George
My name is I-ride-whales.
My name is Jump-the-chimney
My name is Bite-my-knee
My name is Jiggery-pokery
And Riddle-me-ree,
and me

Pauline Clarke

NO HARM DONE

As I went out
The other day,
My head fell off
And rolled away.

But when I noticed
It was gone,
I picked it up
And put it on.

Anon

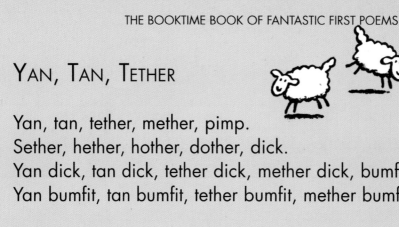

YAN, TAN, TETHER

Yan, tan, tether, mether, pimp.
Sether, hether, hother, dother, dick.
Yan dick, tan dick, tether dick, mether dick, bumfit.
Yan bumfit, tan bumfit, tether bumfit, mether bumfit, gigot.

Anon
Cumbrian way of counting sheep: one to twenty.

ELETELEPHONY

Once there was an elephant,
Who tried to use the telephant –
No! No! I mean an elephone
Who tried to use the telephone –
(Dear me! I am not certain quite
That even now I've got it right.)

Howe'er it was, he got his trunk
Entangled in the telephunk;
The more he tried to get it free,
The louder buzzed the telephee –
(I fear I'd better drop the song
Of elephop and telephong!)

Laura E. Richards

NUTTER

The moon's a big white football,
The sun's a pound of butter.
The earth is going round the twist
And I'm a little nutter!

Kit Wright

AS I WAS GOING UP THE STAIR

As I was going up the stair
I met a man who wasn't there.
He wasn't there again today.
Oh, how I wish he'd go away!

Anon

A Chubby Little Snowman

A chubby little snowman
Had a carrot nose;
Along came a rabbit
And what do you suppose?
That hungry little bunny,
Looking for his lunch,
ATE the snowman's carrot nose ...
Nibble, nibble, CRUNCH!

Anon

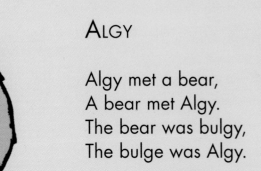

Algy

Algy met a bear,
A bear met Algy.
The bear was bulgy,
The bulge was Algy.

Anon

PLEAS-E!

Bumble bee, bumble bee,
Fly away home;
Leave my naked toes
Alone!

Bumble bee, bumble bee,
Don't you know
Another place where
You can go?

Bumble bee, bumble bee,
When I doze off,
I don't need you, so
Buzz off!

June Crebbin

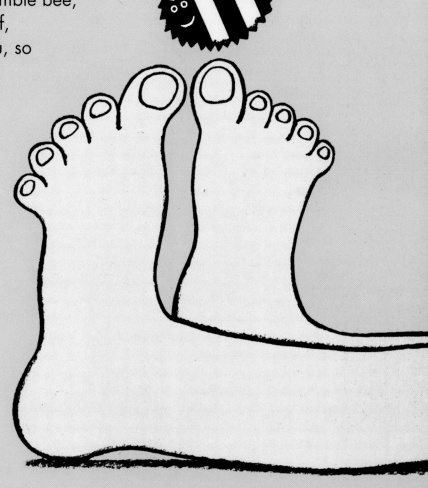

My Dad's Thumb

My dad's thumb
can stick pins in wood
without flinching –
it can crush family-size matchboxes
in one stroke
and lever off jam-jar lids without piercing
at the pierce here sign.

If it wanted
it could be a bath-plug
or a paint-scraper
a keyhole cover or a tap-tightener.

It's already a great nutcracker
and if it dressed up
it could easily pass
as a broad bean or a big toe.

In actual fact, it's quite simply
the world's fastest envelope burster.

Michael Rosen

Who's In?

'The door is shut fast
And everybody's out.
But people don't know
What they're talking about!'
Say the fly on the wall,
And the flame on the coals,
And the dog on his rug,
And the mice in their holes,
And the kitten curled up,
And the spiders that spin -
'What, everyone out?
Why, everyone's in!'

Elizabeth Fleming

The Kettle

There's a little metal kettle
That is sitting near the settle.
You will hear the tittle tattle
Of the lid begin to rattle
When the kettle starts to boil.
What a pretty prittle prattle
Of the kettle near the settle,
Such a merry tittle tattle
When the lid begins to rattle
And the kettle starts to boil.

Gwynneth Thurburn

AWKWARD CHILD

She fell into the bath-tub
She fell into the sink,
She fell into the raspberry jam
And came – out – pink.

Rose Fyleman

A BOY WENT WALKING

One day a boy went walking,
And walked into a store.
He bought a pound of sausage meat,
And laid it on the floor.

The boy began to whistle -
He whistled up a tune,
And all the little sausages
Danced around the room.

Unknown

WITCH, WITCH

'Witch, witch, where do you fly?'...
'Under the clouds and over the sky.'

'Witch, witch, what do you eat?'...
'Little black apples from Hurricane Street.'

'Witch, witch, what do you drink?'...
'Vinegar, blacking and good red ink.'

'Witch, witch, where do you sleep?'...
'Up in the clouds where pillows are cheap.'

Rose Fyleman

FOUR STIFF-STANDERS

Four stiff-standers
Four dilly-danders,
Two lookers,
Two crookers
And a wig-wag.

Traditional

CLOCKS AND WATCHES

Our great
Steeple clock
Goes TICK - TOCK,
TICK - TOCK;

Our small
Mantel clock
Goes TICK-TACK, TICK-TACK,
TICK-TACK, TICK-TACK;

Our little
Pocket watch
Goes Tick-a-tacker, tick-a-tacker
Tick-a-tacker, tick.

Unknown

THERE WAS AN OLD WOMAN

There was an old woman who lived under a hill,
And if she's not gone, she's living there still.

Unknown